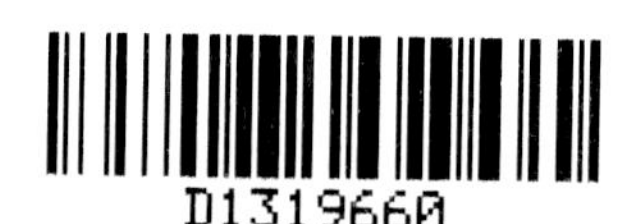

1st Grade

Hooked on Math®

Addition and Subtraction

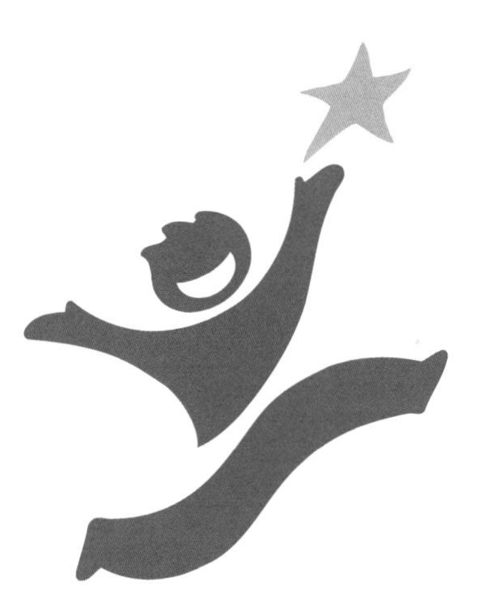

Designed and illustrated by
Big Yellow Taxi, Inc.

The Number Line

Count the numbers in the number line 1 to 20 out loud.

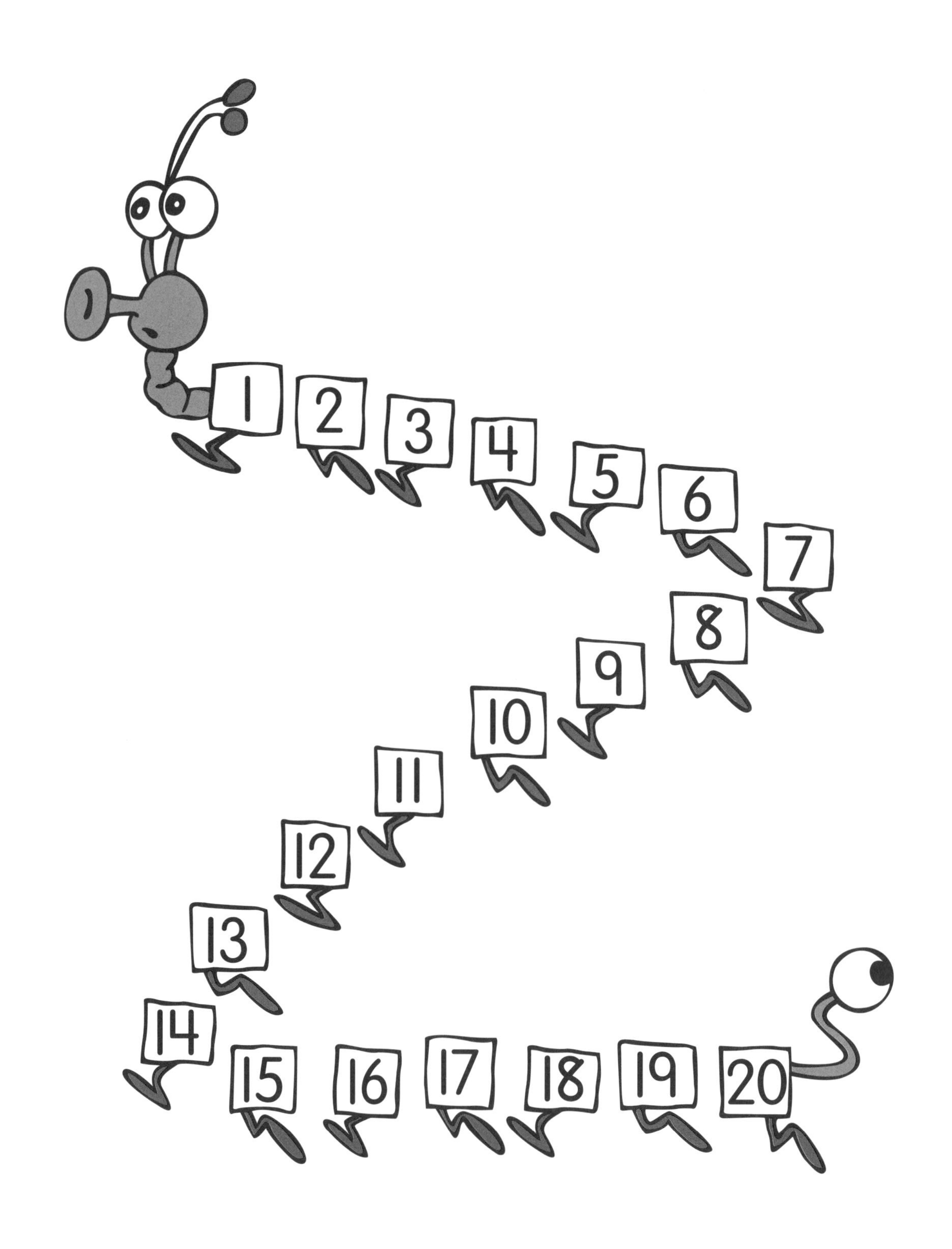

Addition Number Line

Follow the arrows with your finger to count up.

Start → 1, 2, 3, 4, 5, 6, 7, 8, 9, 10, 11, 12, 13, 14, 15, 16, 17, 18, 19, 20

20
19
18
17
16
15
14
13
12
11
10
9
8
7
6
5
4
3
2
1

Start

Subtraction Number Line

Follow the arrows with your finger to count down.

Start

20
19
18
17
16
15
14
13
12
11
10
9
8
7
6
5
4
3
2
1

Solve each problem.
Write the sum on the line.

$1 + 1 =$ ___

$2 + 1 =$ ___

$3 + 1 =$ ___

$4 + 1 =$ ___

$5 + 1 =$ ___

$6 + 1 =$ ___

$7 + 1 =$ ___

$8 + 1 =$ ___

$9 + 1 =$ ___

Star Crossed

I did it!

Solve each problem. Find the matching answer star. Color the stars to match.

Solve each problem.
Write the sum on the line.

$5+2=$ ____

$1+2=$ ____

$6+2=$ ____

$2+2=$ ____

$7+2=$ ____

$3+2=$ ____

$8+2=$ ____

$4+2=$ ____

$9+2=$ ____

Flower Fun

I did it!

Help the alien color the flowers.
Solve each problem.
Match the answer to the Key.
Then color the flower.

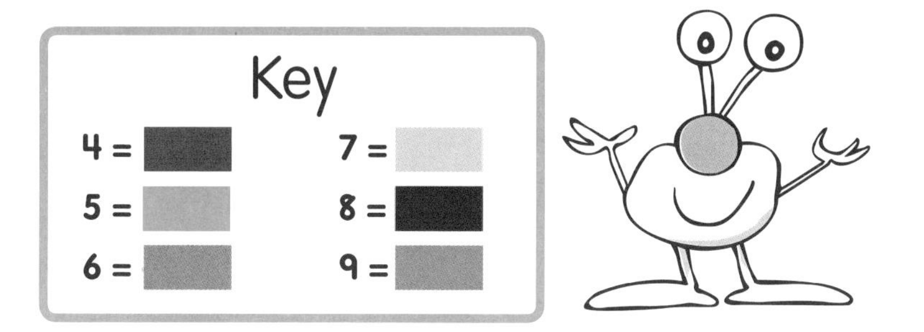

Solve each problem.
Write the sum on the line.

$5 + 3 =$ ____

$1 + 3 =$ ____

$6 + 3 =$ ____

$2 + 3 =$ ____

$7 + 3 =$ ____

$3 + 3 =$ ____

$8 + 3 =$ ____

$4 + 3 =$ ____

$9 + 3 =$ ____

Space Search

Pop Fox is looking for the correct answer.
Draw a path through the maze to find it.

Act It Out

Toss a coin onto these two pages. Where did it land?
Solve the problem.
Skip, blink, clap, whistle, or twirl that many times.

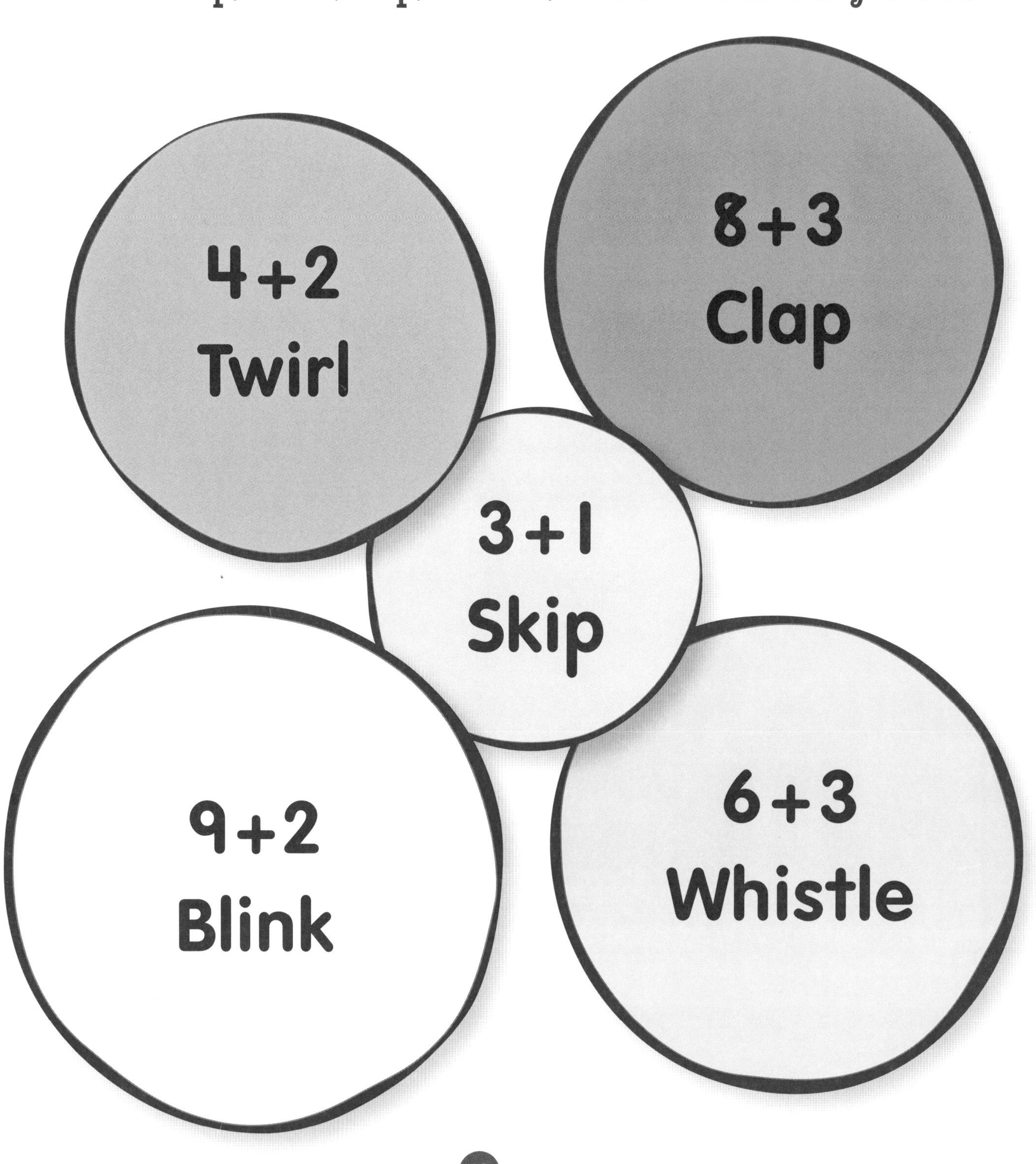

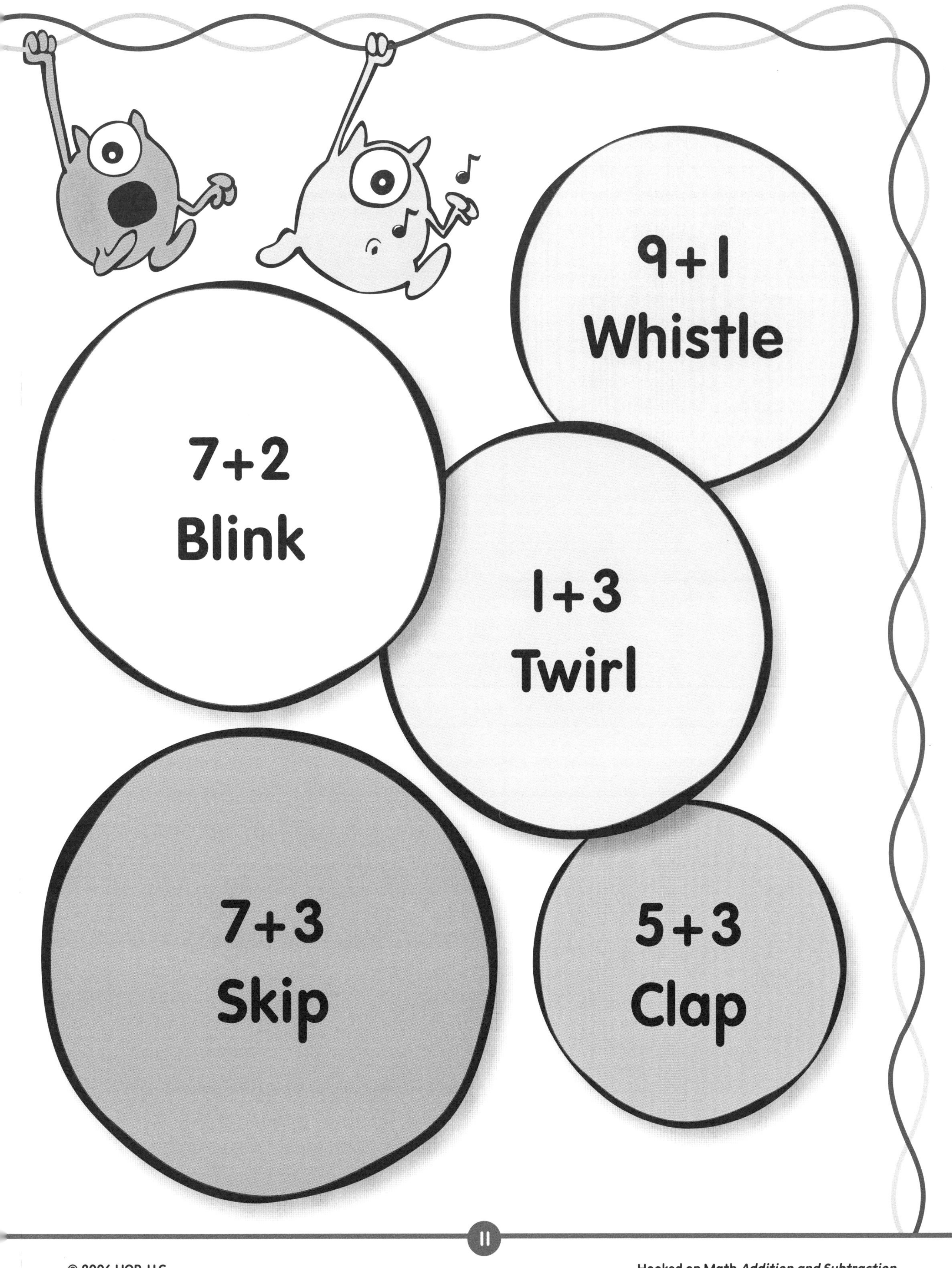
9+1
Whistle
7+2
Blink
1+3
Twirl
7+3
Skip
5+3
Clap

Hats Off!

1 hat

1 hat on a rat.
2 hats on the ground.

3 hats on a rat.
3 hats on the ground.

How many hats?

6 hats on one rat.
3 hats on the other.
9 hats in all.

7 hats on one rat.
2 hats on the other.
How many in all?

9 hats on one rat.
3 hats on the other.
How many in all?

Too many hats!

Solve each problem.
Write the sum on the line.

$5+4=$ ____

$1+4=$ ____

$6+4=$ ____

$2+4=$ ____

$7+4=$ ____

$3+4=$ ____

$8+4=$ ____

$4+4=$ ____

$9+4=$ ____

Add in Space

Add 4 to each of the numbers in a red space.
Write the answers in the blue spaces.

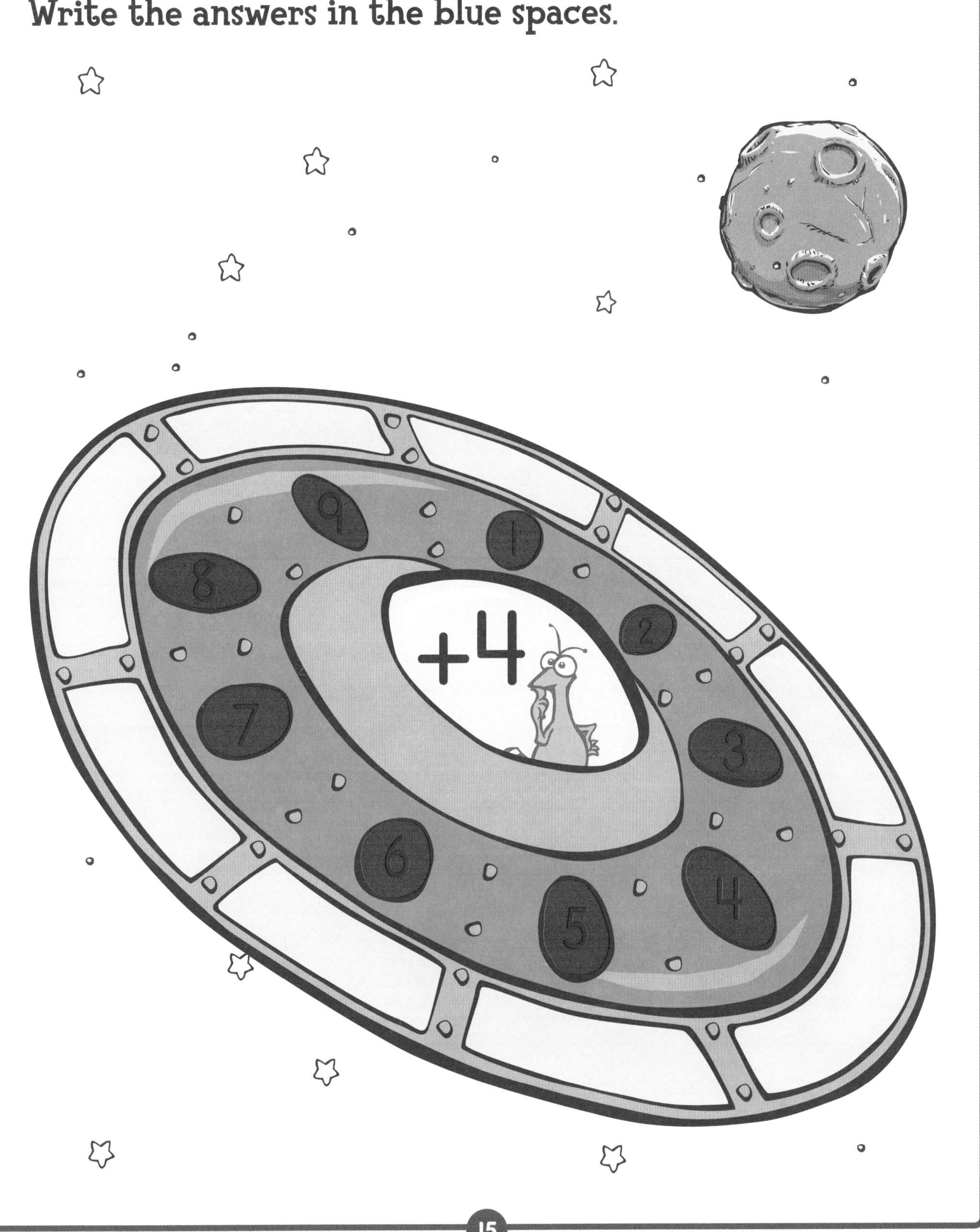

Solve each problem.
Write the sum on the line.

$5 + 5 =$ ____

$1 + 5 =$ ____

$6 + 5 =$ ____

$2 + 5 =$ ____

$7 + 5 =$ ____

$3 + 5 =$ ____

$8 + 5 =$ ____

$4 + 5 =$ ____

$9 + 5 =$ ____

It's Puzzling

Solve each problem.
Draw lines to the correct answers to finish the puzzle.

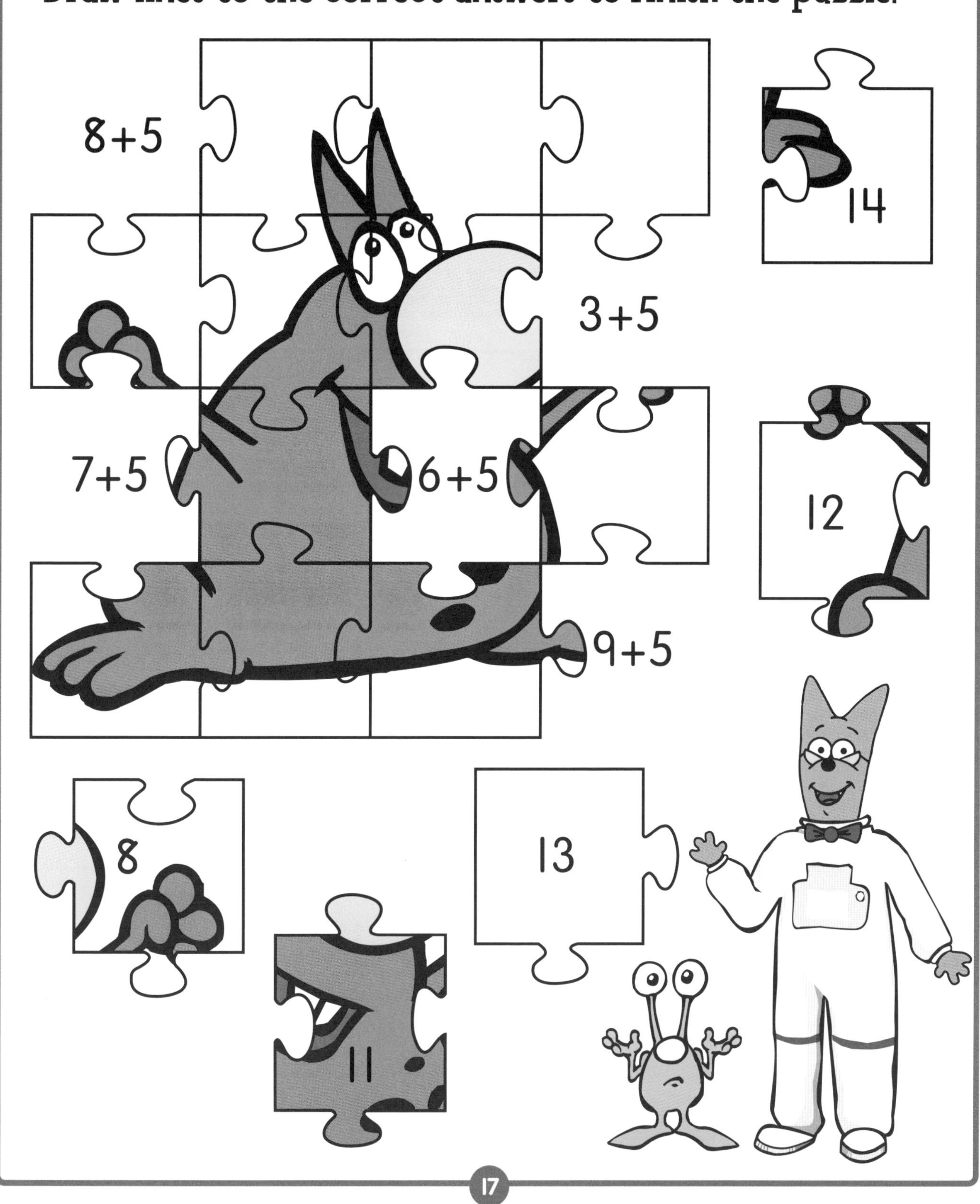

Solve each problem.
Write the sum on the line.

$1 + 6 =$ ____

$2 + 6 =$ ____

$3 + 6 =$ ____

$4 + 6 =$ ____

$5 + 6 =$ ____

$6 + 6 =$ ____

$7 + 6 =$ ____

$8 + 6 =$ ____

$9 + 6 =$ ____

Kite Flight

I did it!

Draw kite strings to the correct answers.
Color each alien to match its kite.

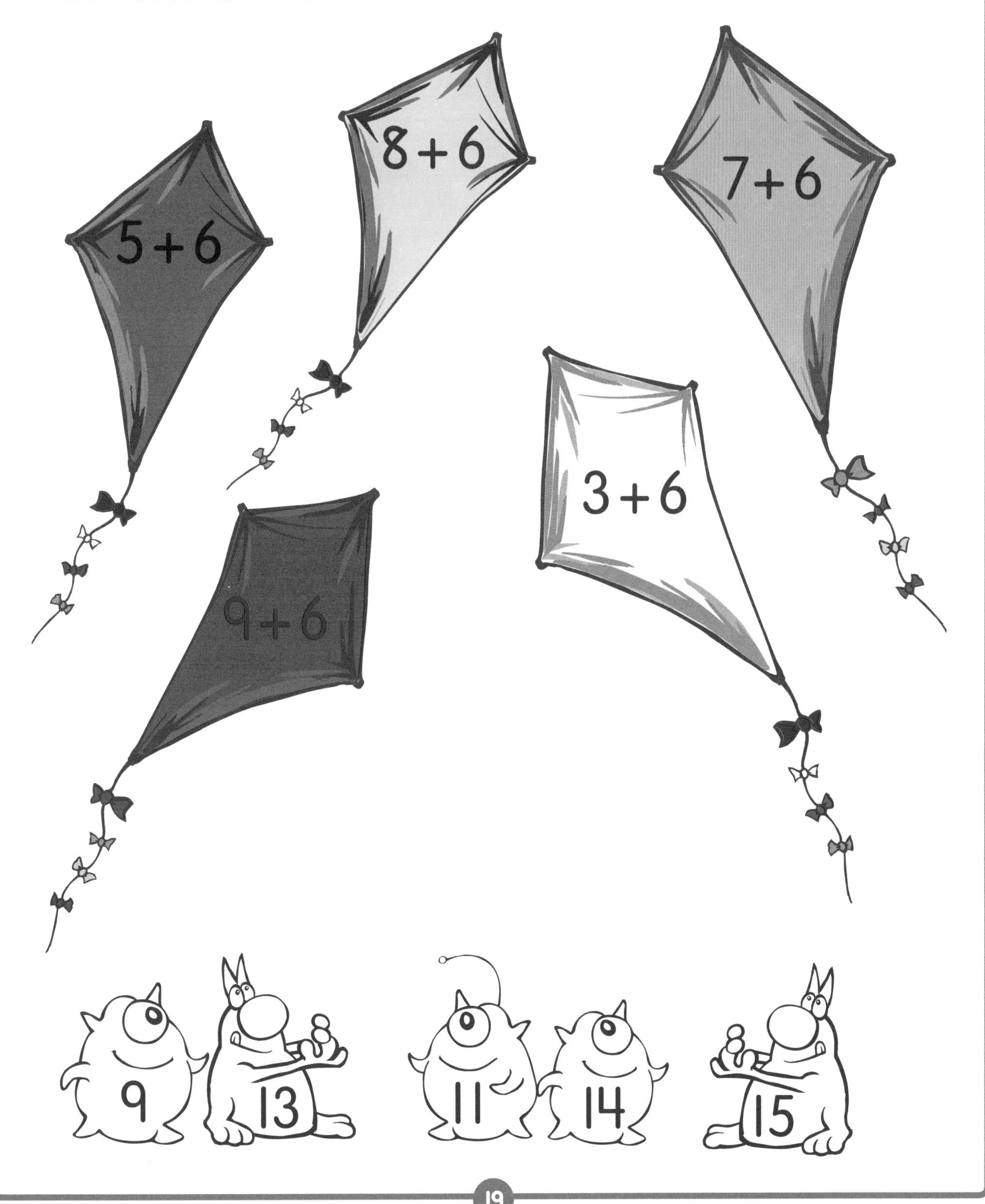

Let's Pretend

Solve one of the problems in the box.
Find the answer and pretend to be the animal in that circle.
Can anyone guess which problem you solved?

Problems

2 + 3

4 + 2

3 + 1

4 + 3

6 + 4

4 + 5

5 + 6

7 + 1

7
8
9
10
11

Dinnertime

Set the dinner table together.

Count all the people who will be eating.

Gather the same number of dishes, silverware, napkins, and glasses.

Note to Parents
You can use the items in each place setting to review simple addition with your child. You might ask, "How many things does each person have?" or "How many forks are on this side of the table?"

Adding Guests

Figure out how many place settings you would need if 4 more people came to dinner.

What would happen if 5 more people came to dinner?

What would happen if 6 more people came to dinner?

Decide if you have enough chairs at the table for each number of guests.

Note to Parents
You can use the addition number line at the beginning of this workbook to help demonstrate addition if your child is having trouble keeping track of the numbers.

Solve each problem.
Write the sum on the line.

$5 + 7 =$ ___

$1 + 7 =$ ___

$6 + 7 =$ ___

$2 + 7 =$ ___

$7 + 7 =$ ___

$3 + 7 =$ ___

$8 + 7 =$ ___

$4 + 7 =$ ___

$9 + 7 =$ ___

Shhh!

I did it!

How do you get a baby alien to sleep?
Solve each problem.
Then match the answers to the Key.
Write the letters in order on the lines.

6+7 ____ 2+7 ____ 8+7 ____ 3+7 ____ –

4+7 ____ 9+7 ____ !

Key

9	10	11	13	15	16
O	K	E	R	C	T

Solve each problem.
Write the sum on the line.

$5+8=$ ____

$1+8=$ ____

$6+8=$ ____

$2+8=$ ____

$7+8=$ ____

$3+8=$ ____

$8+8=$ ____

$4+8=$ ____

$9+8=$ ____

Tag, You're It!

I did it!

The aliens are playing tag.
Who will tag the tree?
Draw a path through the maze to find out.

Solve each problem.
Write the sum on the line.

$5 + 9 =$ ____

$1 + 9 =$ ____

$6 + 9 =$ ____

$2 + 9 =$ ____

$7 + 9 =$ ____

$3 + 9 =$ ____

$8 + 9 =$ ____

$4 + 9 =$ ____

$9 + 9 =$ ____

Blastoff!

Draw a line from each alien to the correct answer.
Color each spaceship to match its alien.

Add and Match

Find a pair of matching pictures.
Add the numbers on the two cards.
Point to the answer in the box on the next page.

14 12 15 16 11 13

Have a Ball

6 balls in the air.
4 balls on the ground.
How many balls in all?

3 balls on the left.
7 balls on the right.
How many balls in all?

2 balls on a head.
8 balls on a foot.
How many balls in all?

No more balls for
the aliens!

Rat Trap

2 balls for one brother.
8 balls for another.
10 balls in all.

9 balls for one brother.
1 ball for the others.
How many balls in all?

7 balls up high.
3 balls down low.
How many balls in all?

No more balls for the brothers! How many balls for the alien?

Solve each problem.
Write the difference on the line.

5 - 1 = ___

9 - 1 = ___

4 - 1 = ___

8 - 1 = ___

3 - 1 = ___

7 - 1 = ___

2 - 1 = ___

6 - 1 = ___

1 - 1 = ___

Wheel of Subtraction

I did it!

Subtract 1 from each number in a green circle.
Write the answer in the yellow wheel.

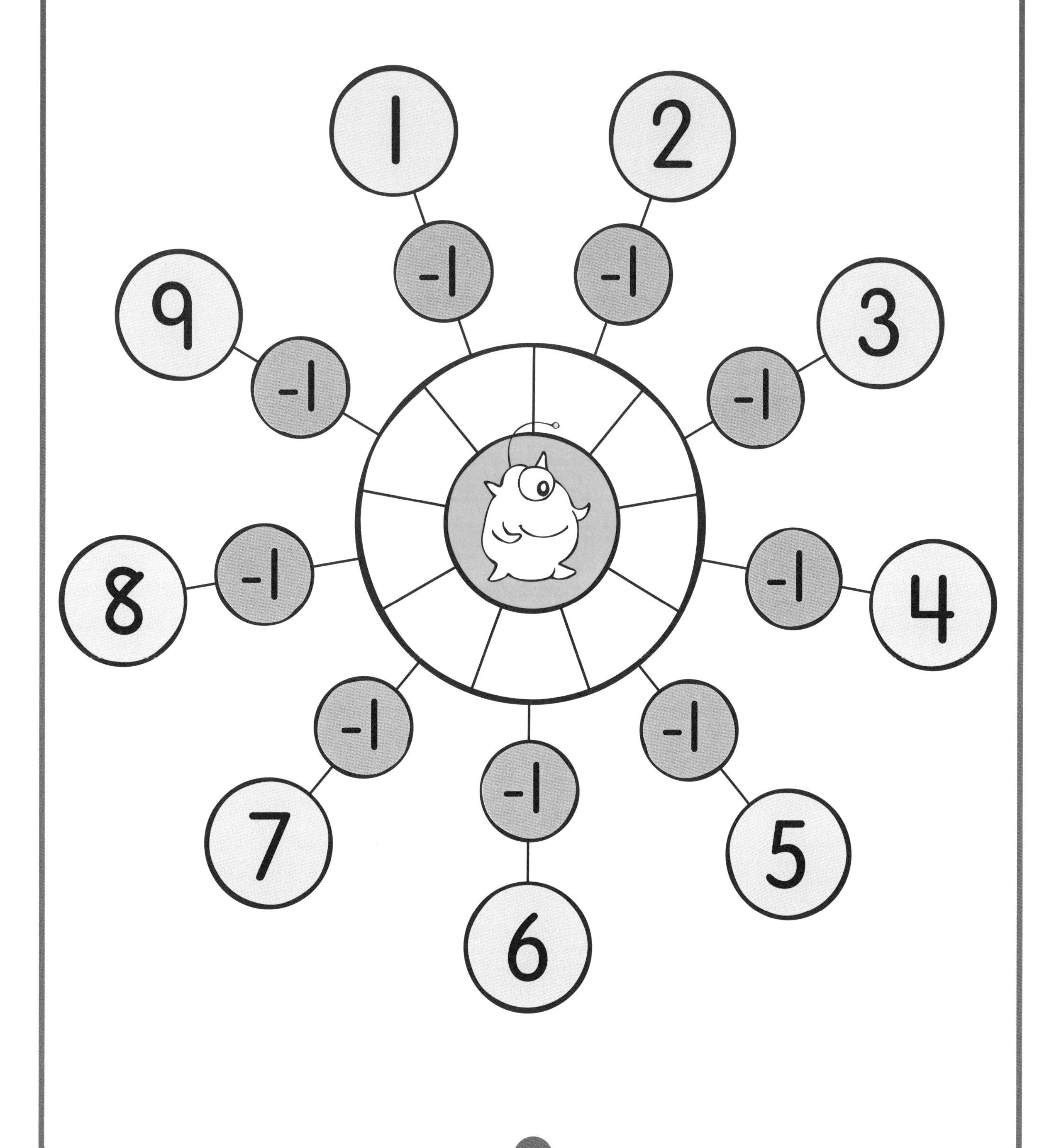

Solve each problem.
Write the difference on the line.

9 - 2 = ___

5 - 2 = ___

8 - 2 = ___

4 - 2 = ___

7 - 2 = ___

3 - 2 = ___

6 - 2 = ___

2 - 2 = ___

And They're Off!

I did it!

Take each alien across the finish line.
Draw a line to match each car to the correct answer.

3

Solve each problem.
Write the difference on the line.

6 - 3 = ___

9 - 3 = ___

5 - 3 = ___

8 - 3 = ___

4 - 3 = ___

7 - 3 = ___

3 - 3 = ___

Take the Cupcake

I did it!

Solve each problem.
Draw lines to the correct answers.

6 - 3

8 - 3

9 - 3

3 - 3

5 - 3

Let's Pretend

Solve one of the problems in the box.
Find the answer and pretend to be the animal in that circle.
Can anyone guess which problem you solved?

Problems
4 - 2
5 - 1
4 - 3
6 - 3
8 - 3
9 - 1
9 - 2
7 - 1

4
5
6
7
8

Family Fun

Musical Chairs

This is a game for two or more players.

How to play:

Use 1 fewer chairs than the number of players.

For 6 players, use 5 chairs. For 5 players, use 4 chairs.

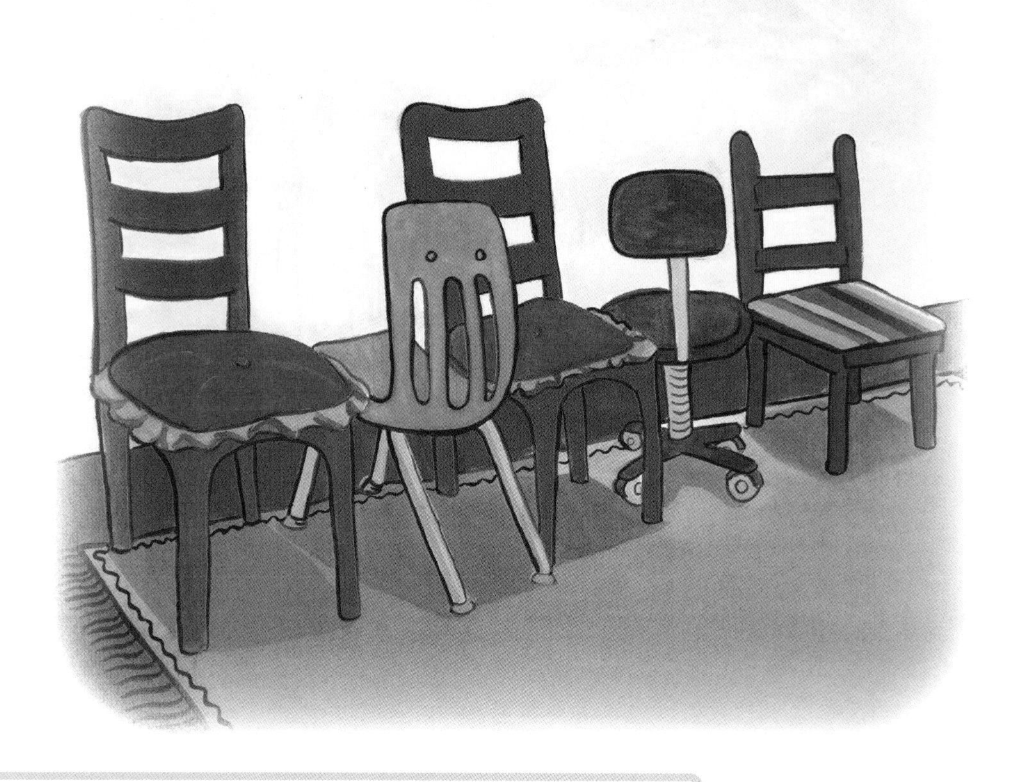

Note to Parents
If you don't have enough family members to play, play a pretend game of musical chairs with dolls or stuffed animals. You could also play a subtraction game by making up a story. You might say, "There are five toys on chairs, but two had to go to the store to get milk for tea. How many toys are left?"

Ask someone to start and stop music during the game.

As the music plays, players should walk around the chairs.

When the music stops, players should scramble to sit in a chair.

The player who can't find a chair is out.

Take 1 chair away each time the music stops.

Count how many chairs are left.

Count the total number of chairs that have been taken away.

Note to Parents
You can use the subtraction number line at the beginning of this book to help demonstrate subtraction if your child is having trouble keeping track of the numbers.

Solve each problem.
Write the difference on the line.

9 - 4 = ___ 6 - 4 = ___

8 - 4 = ___ 5 - 4 = ___

7 - 4 = ___ 4 - 4 = ___

Up, Up, and Away

Solve each problem.
Find the matching answer balloon.
Color the balloons to match.

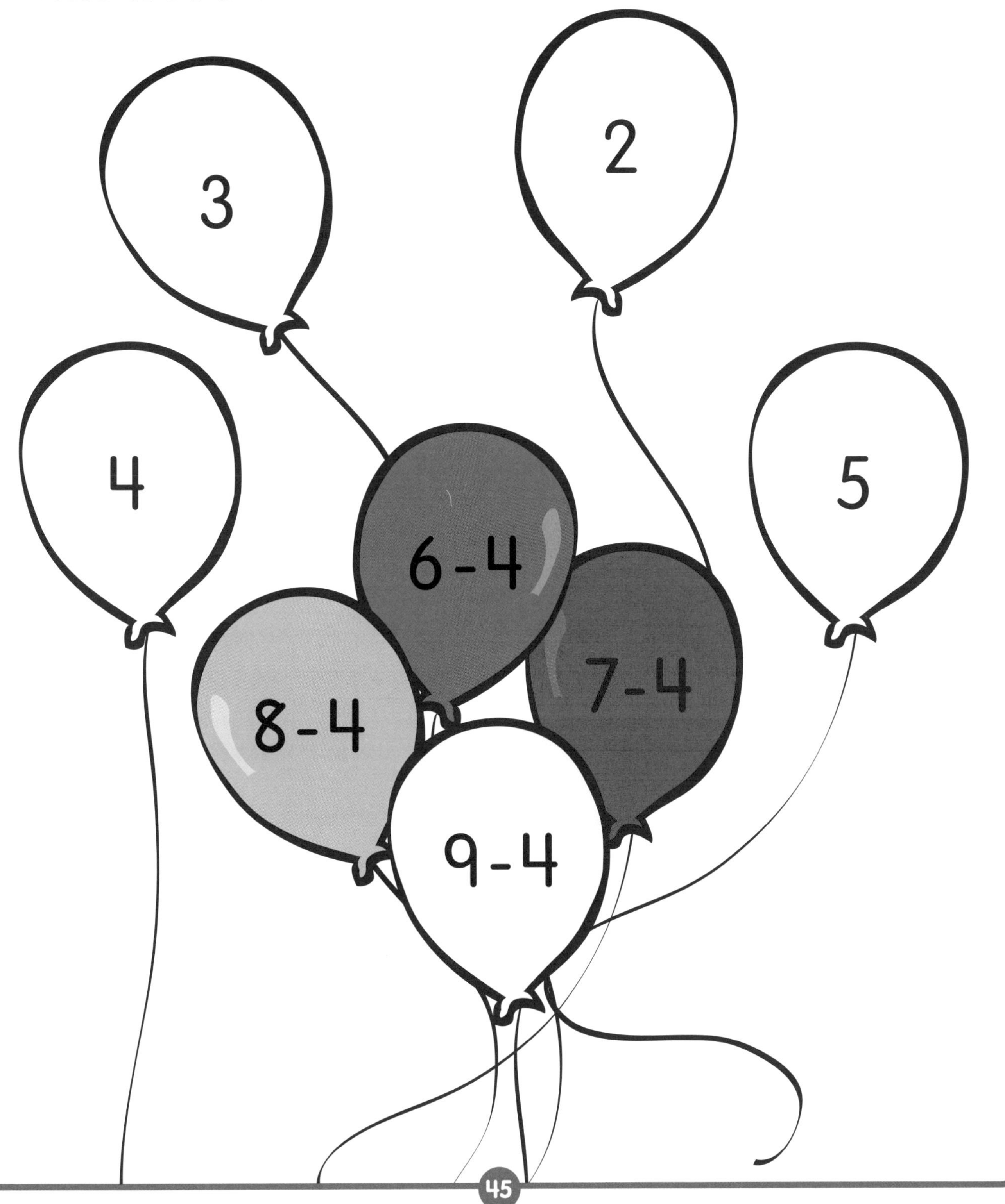

Solve each problem.
Write the difference on the line.

$10 - 5 =$ ____ $7 - 5 =$ ____

$9 - 5 =$ ____ $6 - 5 =$ ____

$8 - 5 =$ ____ $5 - 5 =$ ____

Wheel of Subtraction

I did it!

Subtract 5 from each number in a blue circle.
Write the answer in the orange wheel.

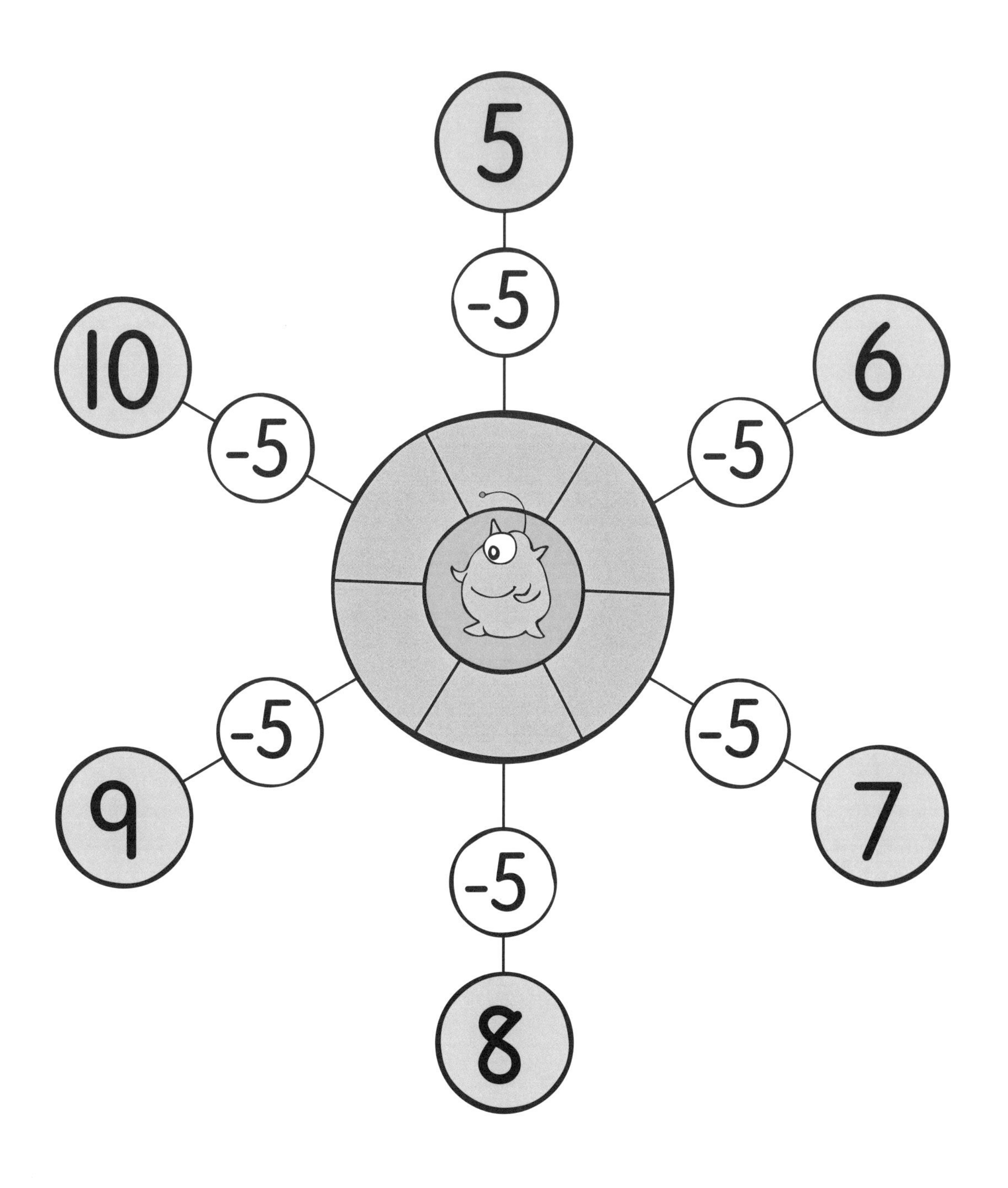

Solve each problem.
Write the difference
on the line.

$12 - 6 =$ ____

$11 - 6 =$ ____

$10 - 6 =$ ____

$9 - 6 =$ ____

$8 - 6 =$ ____

$7 - 6 =$ ____

$6 - 6 =$ ____

Loony Rover

Solve each problem.
Match the answer to the Key.
Then color the rover.

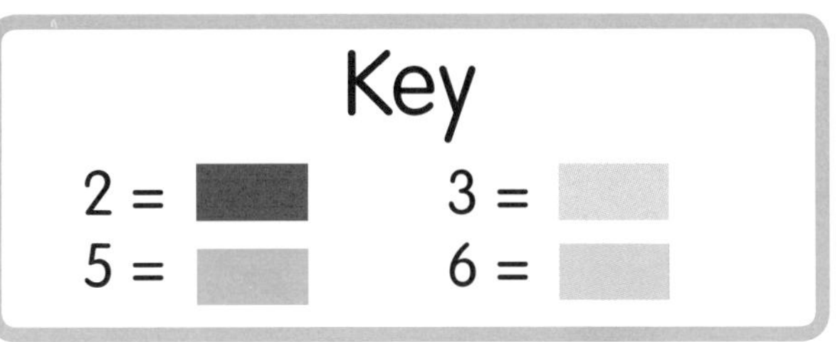

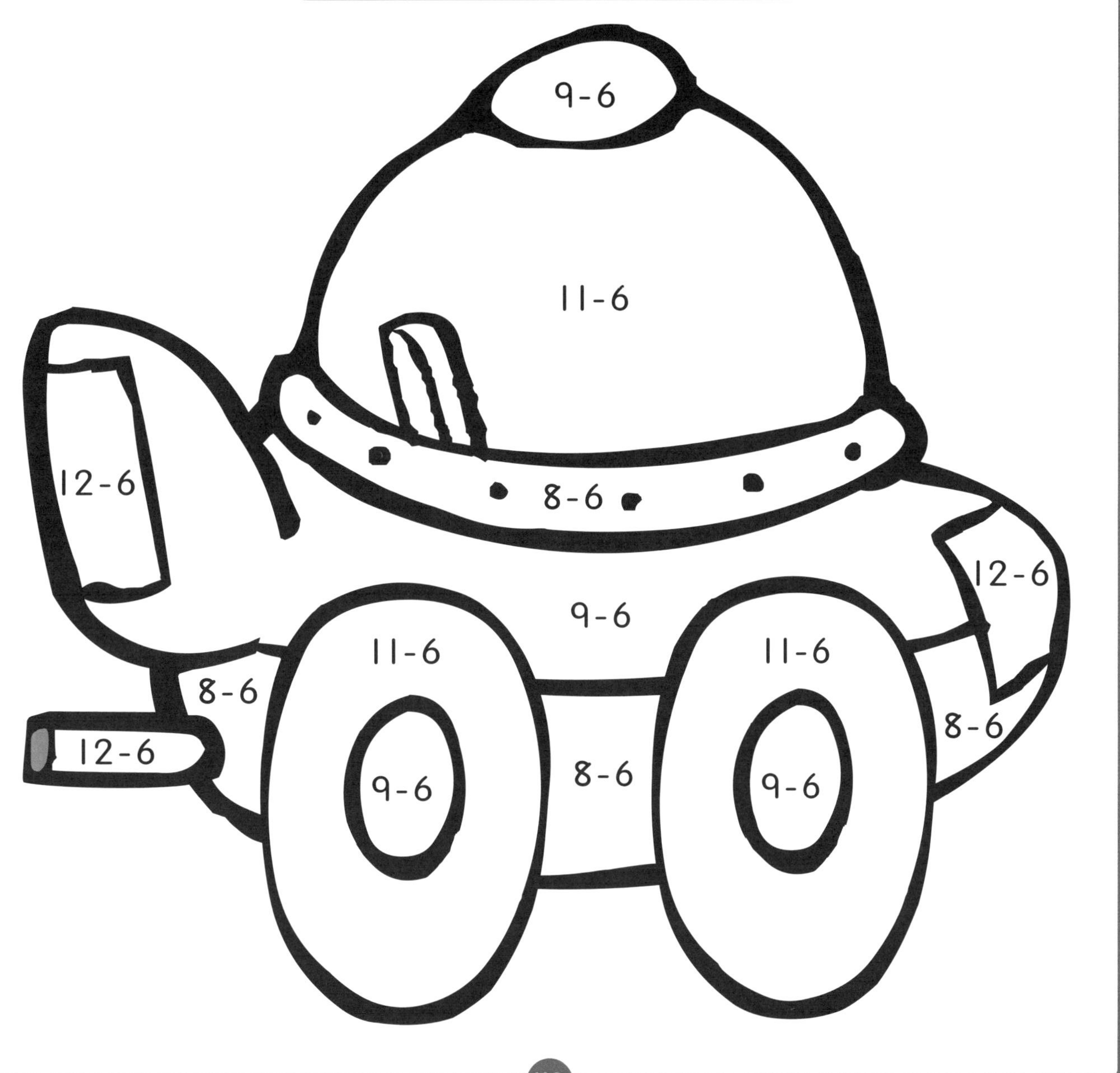

Act It Out

Toss a coin onto these two pages. Where did it land?
Solve the problem.
Jump, stomp, kick, spin, or hop that many times.

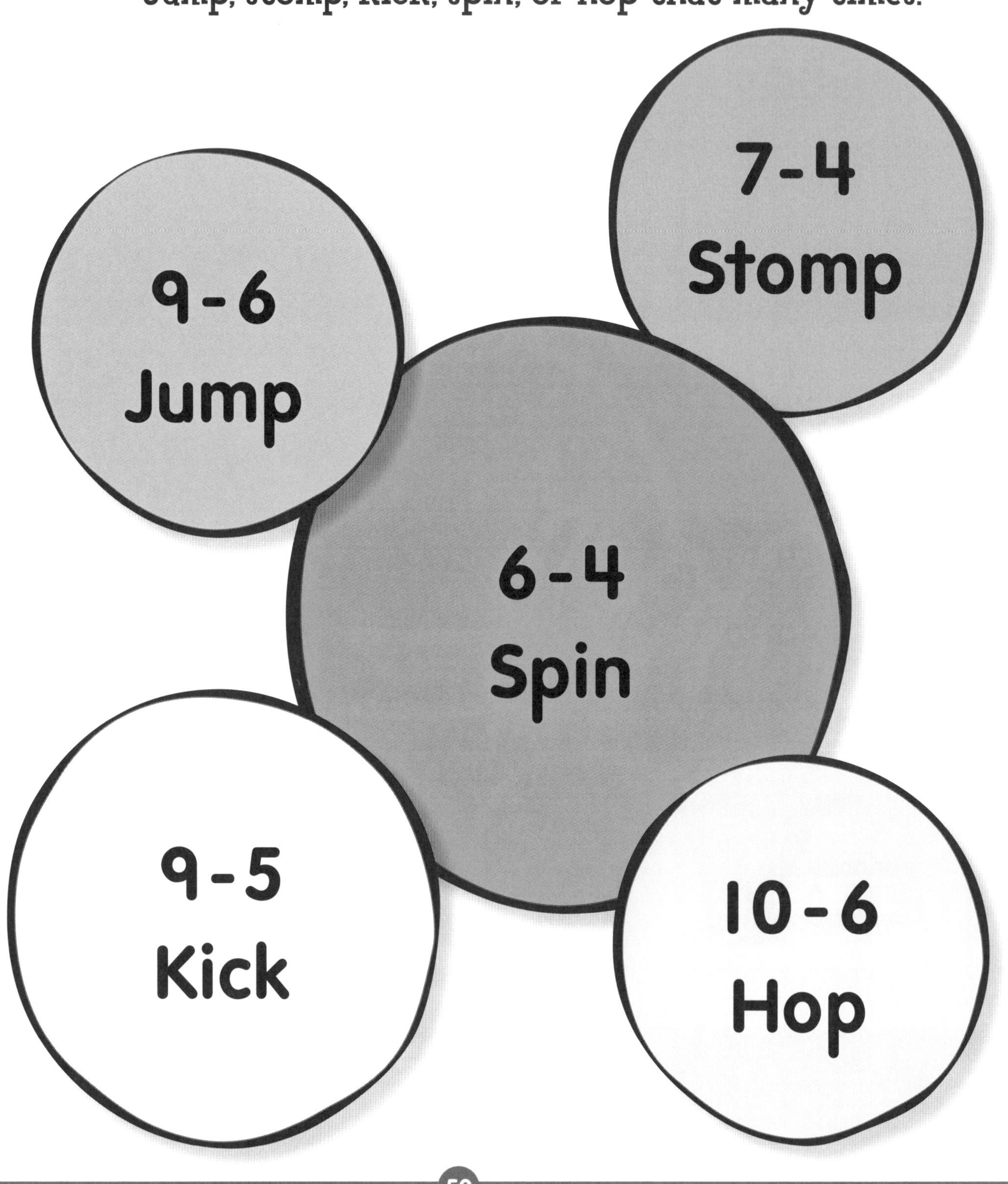

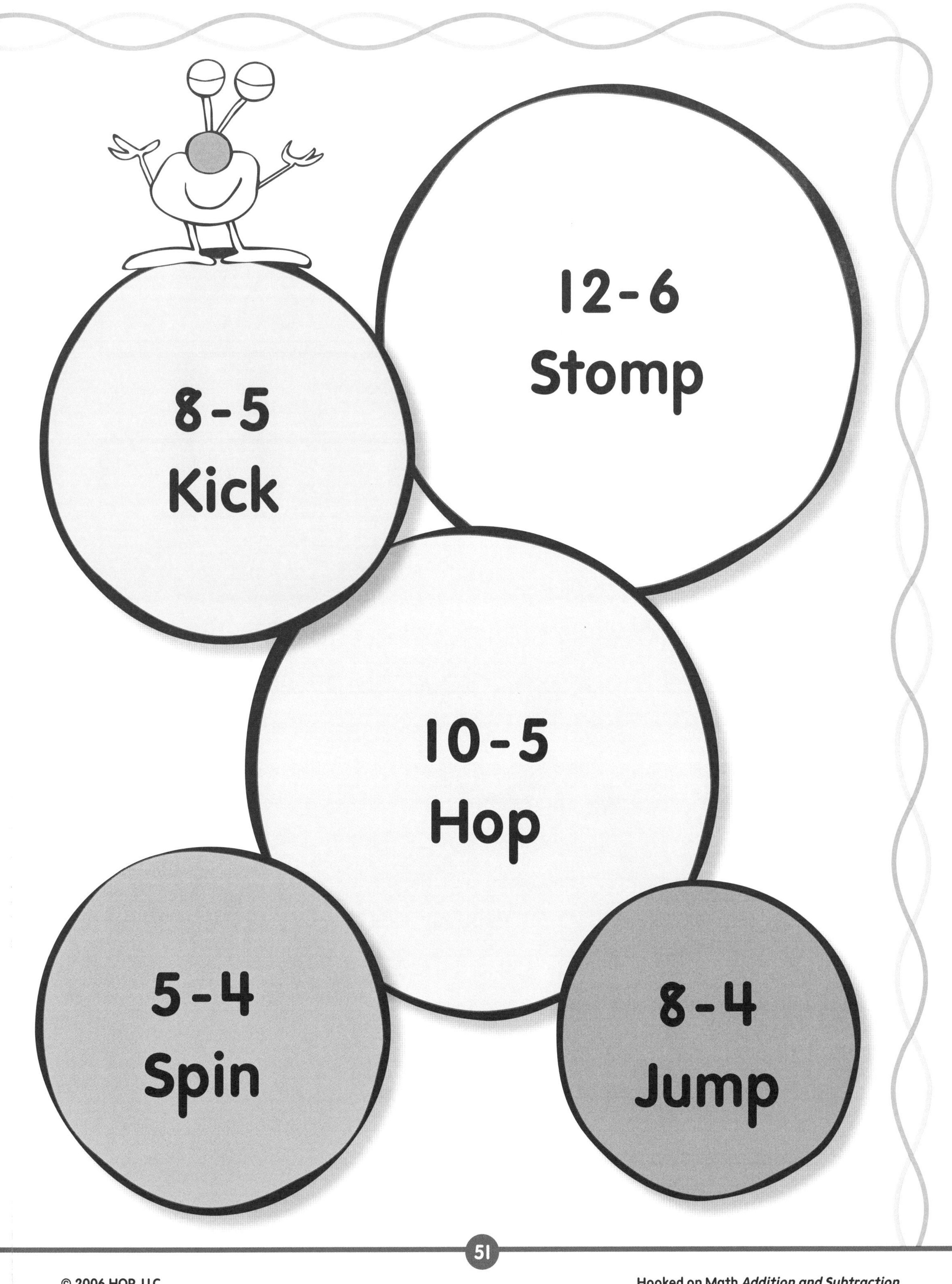
12-6
Stomp
8-5
Kick
10-5
Hop
5-4
Spin
8-4
Jump

Bowled Over

12 bowling pins to start.

4 bowling pins knocked down.
How many pins are left standing?

5 bowling pins knocked down.
How many pins are standing?

Strike!

6 bowling pins knocked down.
How many pins are left standing?

9 bowling pins knocked down.
How many pins are left standing?

Hey, come back with our pins!

Strike!

Solve each problem.
Write the difference on the line.

14 - 7 = ____ 10 - 7 = ____

13 - 7 = ____ 9 - 7 = ____

12 - 7 = ____ 8 - 7 = ____

11 - 7 = ____ 7 - 7 = ____

Go Team!

I did it!

What was the coach looking for in outer space?
Solve each problem.
Then match the answers to the key.
Write the letters in order on the lines.

12-7 ____ 13-7 ____ 13-7 ____ —

11-7 ____ 9-7 ____ 12-7 ____ 10-7 ____ 11-7 ____

Key

2	3	4	5	6
T	R	S	A	L

-8

Solve each problem.
Write the difference on the line.

$12 - 8 =$ ____

$16 - 8 =$ ____

$11 - 8 =$ ____

$15 - 8 =$ ____

$10 - 8 =$ ____

$14 - 8 =$ ____

$9 - 8 =$ ____

$13 - 8 =$ ____

$8 - 8 =$ ____

It's Puzzling

I did it!

Solve each problem.
Draw lines to the correct answers to finish the puzzle.

Solve each problem.
Write the difference on the line.

$18 - 9 =$ ____

$17 - 9 =$ ____

$16 - 9 =$ ____

$15 - 9 =$ ____

$14 - 9 =$ ____

$13 - 9 =$ ____

$12 - 9 =$ ____

$11 - 9 =$ ____

$10 - 9 =$ ____

$9 - 9 =$ ____

Boot Up

I did it!

Solve each problem. Find the matching answer boot. Color the boots to match.

Space Race

Solve the first problem. Move that number of spaces. Solve the problem in the space you land on. If all of your answers are correct, you'll land right on the last square. Good for you, you win!

Start

10 - 8	12 - 9	8 - 7
		10 - 7
		11 - 9

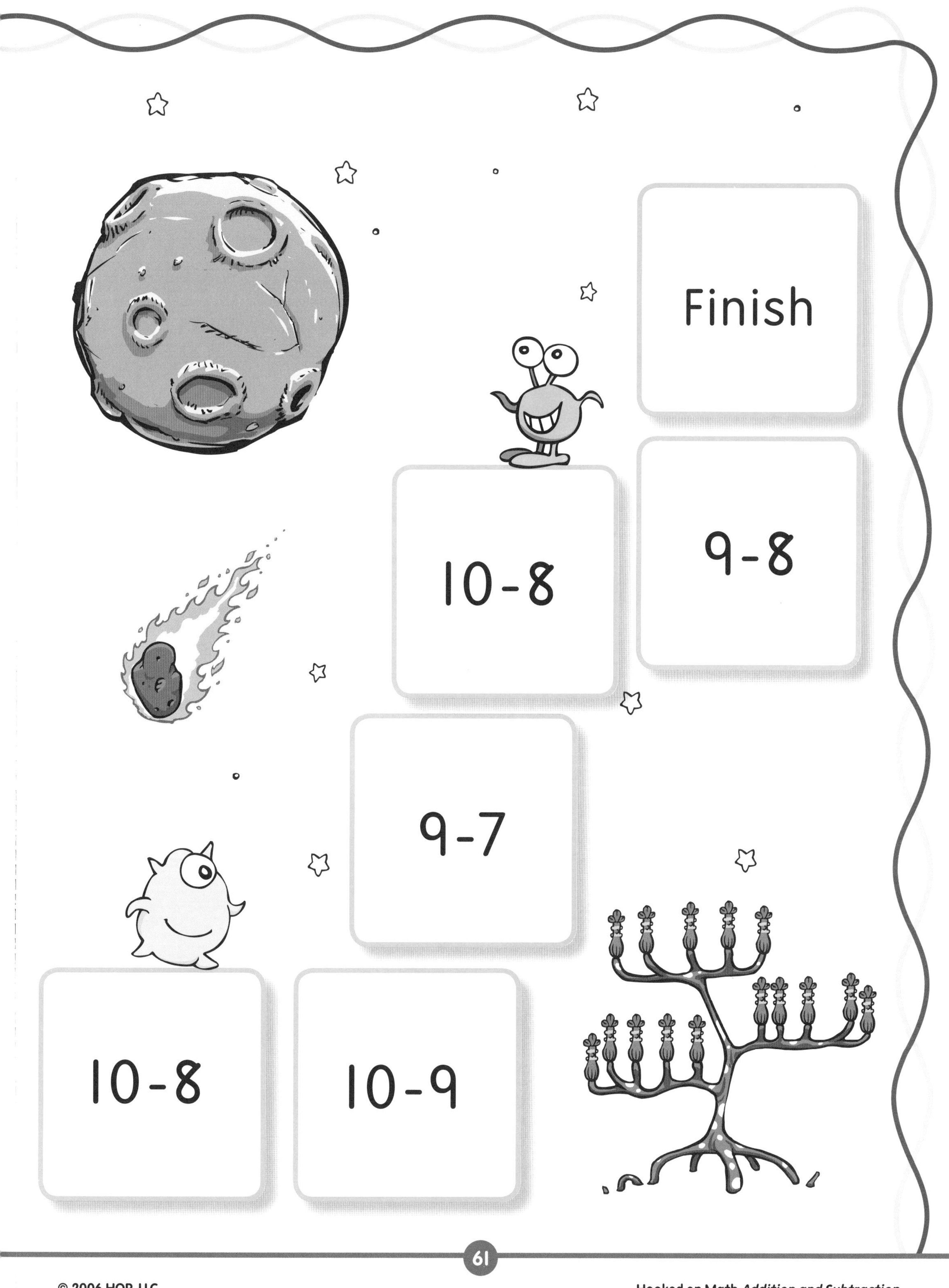
Finish
10-8
9-8
9-7
10-8
10-9

Answer Key

PAGE 4
1 + 1 = 2
2 + 1 = 3
3 + 1 = 4
4 + 1 = 5
5 + 1 = 6
6 + 1 = 7
7 + 1 = 8
8 + 1 = 9
9 + 1 = 10

PAGE 5

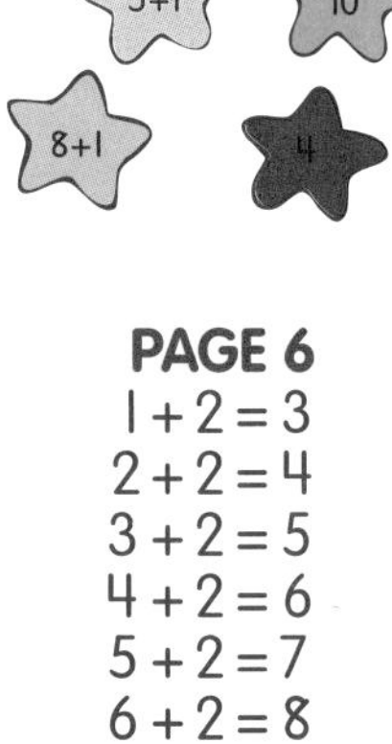

PAGE 6
1 + 2 = 3
2 + 2 = 4
3 + 2 = 5
4 + 2 = 6
5 + 2 = 7
6 + 2 = 8
7 + 2 = 9
8 + 2 = 10
9 + 2 = 11

PAGE 7

PAGE 8
1 + 3 = 4
2 + 3 = 5
3 + 3 = 6
4 + 3 = 7
5 + 3 = 8
6 + 3 = 9
7 + 3 = 10
8 + 3 = 11
9 + 3 = 12

PAGE 9

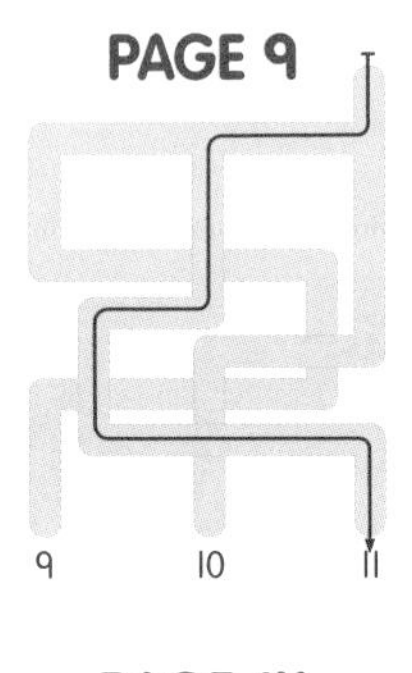

PAGE 14
1 + 4 = 5
2 + 4 = 6
3 + 4 = 7
4 + 4 = 8
5 + 4 = 9
6 + 4 = 10
7 + 4 = 11
8 + 4 = 12
9 + 4 = 13

PAGE 15

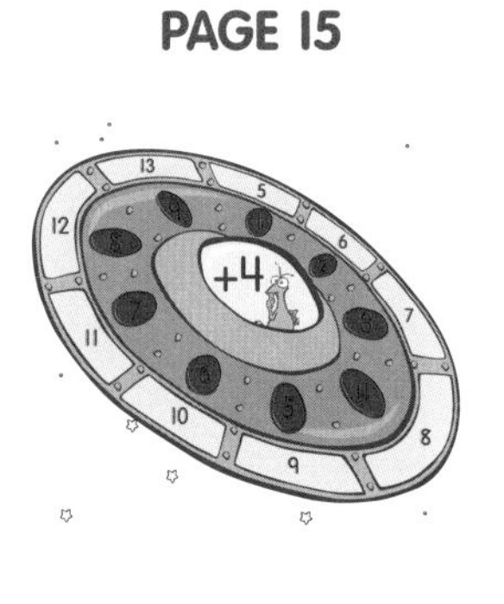

PAGE 16
1 + 5 = 6
2 + 5 = 7
3 + 5 = 8
4 + 5 = 9
5 + 5 = 10
6 + 5 = 11
7 + 5 = 12
8 + 5 = 13
9 + 5 = 14

PAGE 17

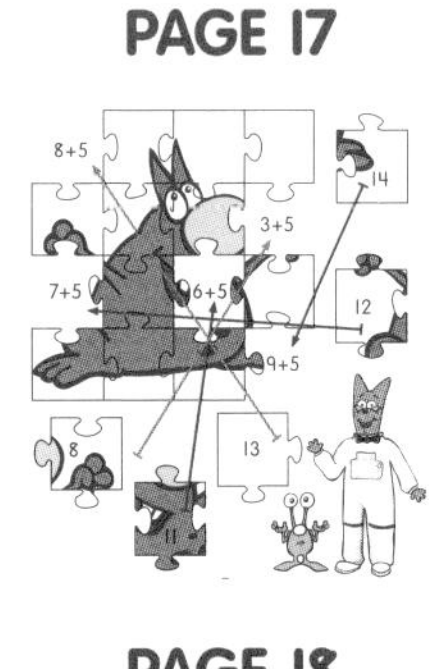

PAGE 18
1 + 6 = 7
2 + 6 = 8
3 + 6 = 9
4 + 6 = 10
5 + 6 = 11
6 + 6 = 12
7 + 6 = 13
8 + 6 = 14
9 + 6 = 15

PAGE 19

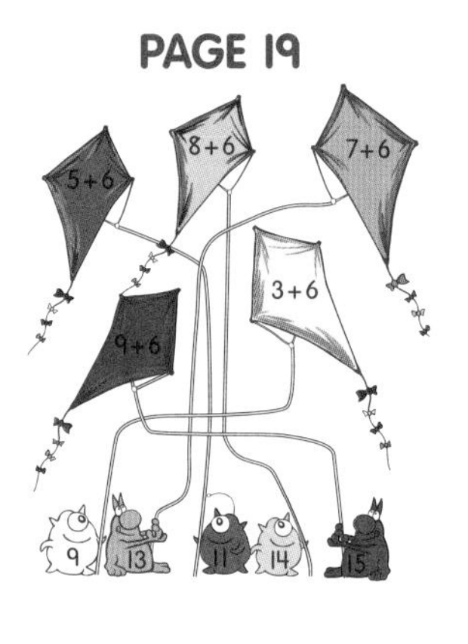

PAGE 24
1 + 7 = 8
2 + 7 = 9
3 + 7 = 10
4 + 7 = 11
5 + 7 = 12
6 + 7 = 13
7 + 7 = 14
8 + 7 = 15
9 + 7 = 16

PAGE 25
6 + 7 = 13
2 + 7 = 9
8 + 7 = 15
3 + 7 = 10
4 + 7 = 11
9 + 7 = 16
ROCK-ET!

PAGE 26
1 + 8 = 9
2 + 8 = 10
3 + 8 = 11
4 + 8 = 12
5 + 8 = 13
6 + 8 = 14
7 + 8 = 15
8 + 8 = 16
9 + 8 = 17

PAGE 27

PAGE 28

1 + 9 = 10
2 + 9 = 11
3 + 9 = 12
4 + 9 = 13
5 + 9 = 14
6 + 9 = 15
7 + 9 = 16
8 + 9 = 17
9 + 9 = 18

PAGE 29

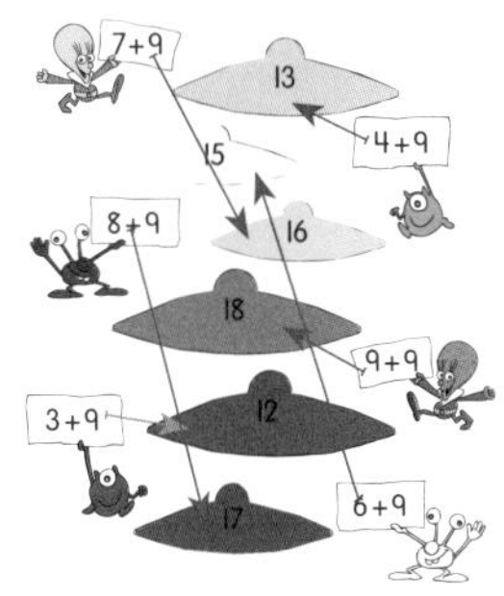

PAGE 34

9 - 1 = 8
8 - 1 = 7
7 - 1 = 6
6 - 1 = 5
5 - 1 = 4
4 - 1 = 3
3 - 1 = 2
2 - 1 = 1
1 - 1 = 0

PAGE 35

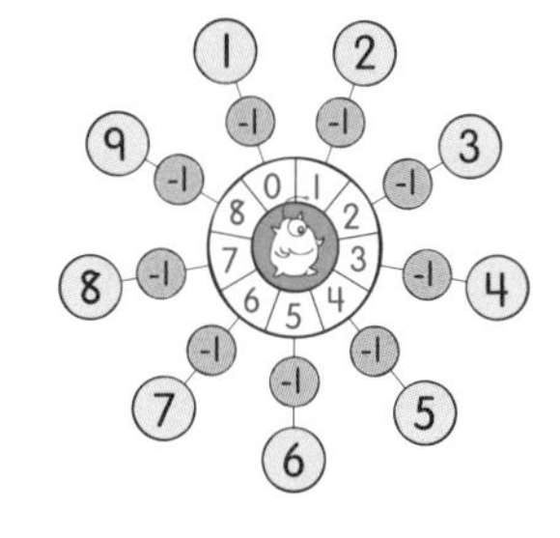

PAGE 36

9 - 2 = 7
8 - 2 = 6
7 - 2 = 5
6 - 2 = 4
5 - 2 = 3
4 - 2 = 2
3 - 2 = 1
2 - 2 = 0

PAGE 37

FINISH!
9-2
7-2
5-2
3
7
5

PAGE 38

9 - 3 = 6
8 - 3 = 5
7 - 3 = 4
6 - 3 = 3
5 - 3 = 2
4 - 3 = 1
3 - 3 = 0

PAGE 39

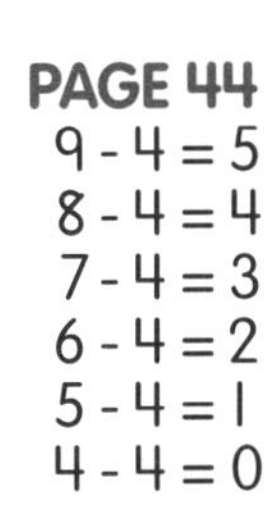

PAGE 44

9 - 4 = 5
8 - 4 = 4
7 - 4 = 3
6 - 4 = 2
5 - 4 = 1
4 - 4 = 0

PAGE 45

PAGE 46

10 - 5 = 5
9 - 5 = 4
8 - 5 = 3
7 - 5 = 2
6 - 5 = 1
5 - 5 = 0

PAGE 47

5
10
6
9
7
8

PAGE 48

12 - 6 = 6
11 - 6 = 5
10 - 6 = 4
9 - 6 = 3
8 - 6 = 2
7 - 6 = 1
6 - 6 = 0

PAGE 49

PAGE 54

14 - 7 = 7
13 - 7 = 6
12 - 7 = 5
11 - 7 = 4
10 - 7 = 3
9 - 7 = 2
8 - 7 = 1
7 - 7 = 0

PAGE 55

12 - 7 = 5
13 - 7 = 6
13 - 7 = 6
11 - 7 = 4
9 - 7 = 2
12 - 7 = 5
10 - 7 = 3
11 - 7 = 4
ALL-STARS

PAGE 56

16 - 8 = 8
15 - 8 = 7
14 - 8 = 6
13 - 8 = 5
12 - 8 = 4
11 - 8 = 3
10 - 8 = 2
9 - 8 = 1
8 - 8 = 0

PAGE 57

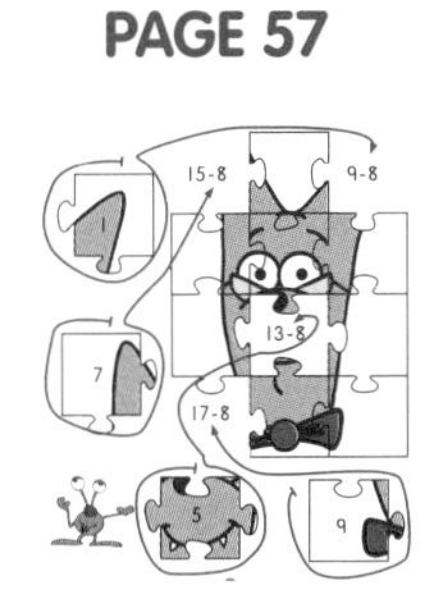

PAGE 58

18 - 9 = 9
17 - 9 = 8
16 - 9 = 7
15 - 9 = 6
14 - 9 = 5
13 - 9 = 4
12 - 9 = 3
11 - 9 = 2
10 - 9 = 1
9 - 9 = 0

PAGE 59

I did it!

Congratulations!

has successfully completed this workbook.